Supplement to the Annotated Catalogue of the H. Colin Slim

STRAVINSKY
COLLECTION

DONATED BY PROFESSOR SLIM
TO THE UNIVERSITY OF
BRITISH COLUMBIA LIBRARY

THE UNIVERSITY OF BRITISH COLUMBIA
Library

ACKNOWLEDGMENTS

The author owes a particular debt of gratitude to Kevin Madill, the Music Librarian at the University of British Columbia, for his efforts in advancing the publication of this monograph.

The H. Colin Slim Stravinsky Collection is one of the treasures of the UBC Library. It includes letters, autograph scores, books, and musical quotations representing every period of the composer's life. UBC Library published the original version of this annotated catalogue in 2002, and it is an honour to partner again with Dr. Slim to produce this supplement. This publication is a celebration of a lifelong commitment to Stravinsky, and also signifies Dr. Slim's strong connection to UBC as an alumnus. Dr. Slim's interest in Stravinsky began while he was a teenager in Vancouver, but it progressed and deepened during his years as a music student at UBC. That foundation helped to build Dr. Slim's life as a musicologist and widely published scholar. It also helped to spark his lifelong interest in collecting, as well as his desire to enhance the UBC environment for future students. In sharing this collection through his donation, Dr. Slim lends his confidence and support to UBC, the UBC Library, and UBC students. By making the annotated catalogue and its supplement available at no charge to institutions and conservatories, Dr. Slim has given a gift to music lovers, performers, and researchers everywhere.

Susan E. Parker
University Librarian

Conspectus

Section 2

Corrections and additions to Slim, Annotated Catalogue (2002) / 35

Catalogue Notes

Each entry consists of a detailed transcription and, where necessary, translation. In transcriptions, neither Stravinsky's linguistic errors in French and English, nor his frequent omissions of French accents, have been rectified. Translation from the French is by Leonard W. Johnson.

Each entry is preceded by a description and followed by acquisition information, provenance, commentary, and works consulted. In the description, height precedes width in dimensions. A date in parentheses following a musical composition is its year of completion. References in the works consulted for each entry are presented in full, even though they may be repeated elsewhere. The *sigla* below are used for the most frequently cited materials on Stravinsky. The following abbreviations are used:

btn	between
n.	note or footnote
no., nos.	number, numbers
p., pp.	page, pages
pl., pls.	plate, plates

The use of Roman numerals after an Arabic digit indicates an insertion into the *Annotated Catalogue*'s original numbering system (a numbering system chosen to present items by creation date).

Items catalogued beginning with "RBSC" indicate a numerical system unique to UBC Rare Books and Special Collections. These items belong to the UBC Stravinsky Collection and have been highlighted in this volume due to their significance to the project at hand.

Sigla

ILM	Robert Craft. *An Improbable Life: Memoirs*. Nashville: Vanderbilt University Press, 2002.
JAMS	*Journal of the American Musicological Society*.
SAc	Théodore and Denise Strawinsky. *Au coeur du Foyer: Catherine et Igor Strawinsky 1906–1940*. Bourg-la-Reine, France: ZurfluH, 1998.
SBu	*Dearest Bubushkin: The Correspondence of Vera and Igor Stravinsky, 1921–1954, with Excerpts from Vera Stravinsky's Diaries, 1922–1971*. Edited by Robert Craft. Translated by Lucia Davidova. New York: Thames and Hudson, 1985.
SD&D	Igor Stravinsky and Robert Craft. *Dialogues and a Diary*. Garden City, NY: Doubleday, 1963.
SE&D	Igor Stravinsky and Robert Craft. *Expositions and Developments*. Garden City, NY: Doubleday, 1962; repr. Berkeley and Los Angeles: University of California Press, 1981.
SM&C	Igor Stravinsky and Robert Craft. *Memories and Commentaries*. Garden City, NY: Doubleday, 1960; repr. Berkeley and Los Angeles: University of California Press, 1981.
SP&D	Vera Stravinsky and Robert Craft. *Stravinsky in Pictures and Documents*. New York: Simon and Schuster, 1978.
SP&RK	*I.F. Stravinsky: Perepiska s russkimi korrespondentami: Materiali k biographi*. Edited by Viktor Varunts. Moscow: Kompozitor, 1998–2003. 3 vols. (1882–1912, 1913–22, 1923–39).
SSC	Igor Stravinsky. *Selected Correspondence*. Edited by Robert Craft. New York: Alfred A. Knopf, 1982–85. 3 vols.
SSE	Stephen Walsh. *Stravinsky: The Second Exile: France and America, 1934–1971*. New York: Knopf, 2006.

INTRODUCTION

Vancouver was the first Canadian city to hear any work by Igor Fyodorovich Stravinsky (1882–1971). On 15 January 1917, Pierre Monteux (1875–1964) led two compositions by Frédéric Chopin (1810–49) that Stravinsky had orchestrated early in the spring of 1909 at St. Petersburg for Sergei Diaghilev (1872–1929). Both orchestrations were for the first season in Paris of the Ballets Russes at the Théâtre Châtelet featuring the premiere, on 4 June 1909, of *Les Sylphides*, choreographed by Michel Fokine (1880–1942) and starring Vaslav Nijinsky (1889–1950). He also danced in the sole Vancouver performance of *Les Sylphides* by the Ballets Russes in mid-January 1917 at the old CPR Opera House on the west side of Granville Street, between Georgia and Robson.

Although Stravinsky had conducted in Toronto (1937) and Montreal (1945), he did not lead the Vancouver Symphony Orchestra (VSO) until October 1952, an indirect result of an all-Stravinsky concert the previous April at the University of British Columbia. That concert – in Brock Hall – had featured Canadian premieres of his *Concerto per due pianoforti soli* (1935) and of *Les Noces* (1923), in which I participated as duo-pianist and conductor, respectively. In mid-July 1965, Stravinsky (assisted by Robert Craft [1923–2015]) twice led the VSO, specially augmented for the city's eighth International Festival.

On Sunday morning, 5 October 1952, I drove with Stravinsky from the Hotel Vancouver to the Orpheum Theatre for his final VSO rehearsal. On the evening of 27 January 1966, after singing in two choral-orchestral works he conducted in Los Angeles, I sat next to him backstage and we chatted briefly after a performance of his *Symphony in C* (1940) led by Craft.

These encounters with Stravinsky stimulated my forming the 123-item collection that I gave to UBC in 1994. Since then, other donors (and I) have enriched it, necessitating this supplement. A recent acquisition of the composer's own printed score of *Petrushka* (1911), heavily annotated by him in ink and coloured pencils in preparation for its 1948 revised edition, now joins nine other items (1911–67) concerning his ballet and testifies to the resources of UBC's collection.

The bulk of Stravinsky's *Nachlass* is at Basel, in the Paul Sacher Foundation. Vancouver is the only Canadian city to house a collection devoted to him and his music. UBC's current 143 items compare favourably with smaller collections in US universities and conservatories, and even with major ones in the Morgan Library, the New York Public Library, and the Library of Congress. The UBC Library on the Point Grey campus has become an important North American resource for scholars and music lovers concerned with Stravinsky's life, his works, and both his critical opinions and those of others.

SECTION 1

Twenty New Items (1911–82): Added to
UBC's Stravinsky Collection (as of June 2017)

1i

(1911). *Zhar`-ptitsa / L'Oiseau de Feu [The Firebird]*, 1st ed. (Leipzig and Moscow: P. Jurgenson and Rob. Forberg [1911]; repr. Leipzig and Moscow: Jurgenson [1911–18]), 70 pp., pls. 34903–19, c. 30.4 × 23.5 cm, the composer's piano reduction (finished 21 March 1910) of the entire ballet.

Acquisition: H. Colin Slim in Laguna Beach, CA, in 1997, a gift to him from Dorothy Ellis McQuoid in nearby San Clemente. Muriel Zanger, the owner previous to Mrs. McQuoid, inscribed her name in the upper left corner of the title page. Donated by Professor Slim in 2002.

Commentary

A photograph taken April 1910 in St. Petersburg for *Comoedia Illustré* (Paris) shows left to right: Nikolay Tcherepnin (1873–1945) and Stravinsky seated at the piano, and choreographer Michel Fokine (1880–1942) leaning on it, during a *Firebird* rehearsal at the Catherine Hall (German Club) with Tamara Karsavina (1885–1978) in the title role. The ballet was premiered on 25 June 1910 at the Paris Opera.

 This first edition for piano of the complete ballet appeared in June–July 1911, pls. 34903–19. The orchestral full score was published in 1912, pl. 34920. Another copy of Entry **1i** is in the Jean Gray Hargrove Music Library, University of California, Berkeley, and still another was offered for sale by J. & J. Lubrano in 2002.

 Edwin Evans (1874–1945), who knew Stravinsky from early February 1913 in London, was to use a copy of Entry **1i** twenty years later in his analysis of *Firebird*. See also Entry **111i**, below.

Works Consulted

Craft, Robert. *Stravinsky: The Composer*, vol. IX, CD record booklet. Oakhurst, NJ: Music Masters Classics, 1967. pp. 5–14.

Cyr, Louis. *Stravinsky, L'oiseau de feu: Facsimile Edition of Autograph Full Score*. Geneva: Minkoff, 1985. p. 192.

Evans, Edwin. *Stravinsky: The Fire-Bird and Petrushka*. London: Oxford University Press, 1933. p. 12.

Foster, Andrew R. *Tamara Karsavina: Diaghilev's Ballerina*. London: Foster, 2010. pp. 106, 118, 120–21 (ten persons are identified in I.N. Aleksandrov's rehearsal photograph from *Comoedia Illustré* [May 1910]: 119), 140–43.

Joseph, Charles M. *Stravinsky and the Piano*. Ann Arbor, MI: UMI Research Press, 1983. pp. 252–70.

–. "Stravinsky Manuscripts in the Library of Congress and the Pierpont Morgan Library." *The Journal of Musicology* 1, no. 3 (July 1982): 337 (nos. 4, 5).

–. *Stravinsky's Ballets*. New Haven and London: Yale University Press, 2011. pp. 26–47.

Krasovskaya, Vera. *Nijinsky*. Translated by John E. Bowlt. New York: Schirmer Books, 1979. pp. 97–98 (lower plates).

Lederman, Minna, ed. *Stravinsky in the Theatre*. New York: Farrar, Straus and Giroux, 1949; repr. New York: Da Capo, 1975. pl. [3] btn pp. 170–79.

Lerma, Dominique-René de. *Igor Fedorovitch Stravinsky, 1882–1971: A Practical Guide to Publications of His Music*. Kent, OH: Kent State University Press, 1974. p. 49 (no. O9).

Lubrano, J. & J. *Dance Literature & Music, 16th–20th Centuries*. Great Barrington, MA: 2002, lot 32.

The Mary Flagler Cary Music Collection: Printed Books and Music, Manuscripts, Autograph Letters, Documents, Portraits. New York: Pierpont Morgan Library, 1970. p. 48 (no. 201, a copyist's full orchestral score of the complete *Firebird* ballet with Stravinsky's corrections and additions).

Shepard, John. "L'Oiseau de feu: fac-simile du manuscrit Saint-Pétersbourg, 1909–1910." *Notes: Quarterly Journal of the Music Library Association* 44, no. 4 (June 1988): 804–7.

"Shilling House Applauds the Russian Ballet." *The Christian Science Monitor* (8 October 1913): 11 (about a "new" orchestral suite, played in London).

Slim, H. Colin. *Annotated Catalogue of the H. Colin Slim Stravinsky Collection Donated by Him to the University of British Columbia Library*. Vancouver, BC: University of British Columbia Library, 2002. Entries 1, 6, 48, 61, 71, 111, 115.

SP&D. pp. 24, 55, 58–60, 377–78, 503–5.

SP&RK. vol. 1. pp. 381–82 (n. 3–4), 494, 536 (index: Tcherepnin, N.N.).

SSC. vol. 2. pp. 219–22 (incorrect first plate number).

Steshko, Joni Lynn. "L'Oiseau de feu [1910]." *Notes: Quarterly Journal of the Music Library Association* 54, no. 5 (June 1998): 997–1002.

Street, Donald. "A Forgotten Firebird." *Musical Times* 119, no. 1626 (August 1978): 674–76.

Taruskin, Richard. *Stravinsky and the Russian Traditions*. Berkeley and Los Angeles: University of California Press, 1996. pp. 641–42 and n. 124.

Tompakova, O.M. *Nicolay Nikolayevich Tcherepnin*. Moscow: Musika, 1991. pp. 45 (plate), 53–55, 98 (opus 39).

Walsh, Stephen. *Stravinsky, A Creative Spring: Russia and France, 1882–1934*. New York: Alfred A. Knopf, 1999. p. 159, pl. [6] (bottom) btn pp. 172–73, p. 589 (n. 39).

White, Eric Walter. *Stravinsky: The Composer and His Works*. 2nd ed. Berkeley and Los Angeles: University of California Press, 1979; repr. 1984. p. 182.

41i

(1935). Autograph musical quotation, 27 November 1935, from the fourth (final) movement of the *Concerto per due pianoforti soli*, beginning on the right edge of a Danish newspaper clipping – *Dagens nyheder*, 14 October 1935 – of the composer's photograph taken by Herbert Davidsen (1902–71), 22 March 1934, 8.8 × 7.6 cm (including margins), mounted on and concluding on a sheet, 13.4 × 22.7 cm.

Acquisition: Kirsten Walsh for the UBC Music Library on 4 July 2001 from Lisa Cox, *Music Catalogue* 39 (Devon: Spring 2001), lot 111.
Provenance: Unknown.

Commentary

Davidsen's original photograph, taken after a joint concert for Danish Radio, was of Stravinsky and the composer's countryman Nicolai Malko (1883–1961), a conductor in Denmark, 1928–1939. The Danish newspaper *Dagens nyheder* ran the (solo) photograph four times during 1935, the final time as publicity for Stravinsky's and Samuel Dushkin's concert in Copenhagen on the evening of 14 October (on Dushkin [1891–1976], see Entries 41, **41ii**, and 45). Back in Paris, Stravinsky (or someone else) pasted this newspaper photograph on paper and the composer autographed it for distribution at concerts where he and his pianist son Soulima (1910–94) – on whom, see Entries **43i**, 44, and 82 – were performing the *Concerto per due pianoforti soli* in private homes. This exemplar was perhaps made for an autograph seeker at the home of Winnaretta Singer, la Princesse Edmond de Polignac (1865–1943), on whom, see Entry 34.

Works Consulted

Craft, Robert. "Discoveries in Stravinsky's Sketches." *The Moment of Existence*:

Music, Literature, and the Arts 1990–1995. Nashville and London: Vanderbilt University Press, 1996. p. 275.

Slim, H. Colin. "From Copenhagen and Paris: A Stravinsky Photograph-Autograph at the University of British Columbia." *Notes*: *Quarterly Journal of the Music Library Association* 59, no. 3 (March 2003): 542–55.

41ii

(1936). Typed two-sided single-page letter, 27 × 21 cm, in French, 8 January 1936, to "Mr. S. Dushkin, Ansonia Hôtel New-York" with extensive autograph marginalia in ink on both sides. It is signed: "votre [and in Russian script:] Igor Fedorovich" and dated lower left: "Paris / le 8.I.36," plus a stamped envelope: "Paris VIII 49 Rue La Boetie 10-I /1936." and with a typed address and "s/s COLUMBUS":

Mr. S. Dushkin
Ansonia Hôtel
New-York

Très cher Samski,

J'espère que vous êtes en possession de ma réponse télégraphique ainsi que de ma carte qui était une réponse (un peu plus substantielle q'un simple cable) à votre première dépêche et qui s'était croisée avec votre seconde. Quand vous m'aviez cablé la première fois je me trouvais en Suisse – d'où le retard de la réponse dont veuillez m'excuser.

Vers le nouvel an Mme Bouchoné m'a transmise une proposition télégraphique de Jourok (Manager du Ballet de Montecarlo qui jouait à ce moment au Metropolitan Opera House) – des concerts en octobre et nov./36 pour une somme globale de 6 mille dolars. J'ai demandé Mme Bouchoné de l'envoyer promener: I-mo n'ayant aucune confiance dans ce type, 2-do l'époque d'automne n'étant pas aux Etats-Unis une bonne période et 3-o croyant pouvoir faire mieux que ça en Janv.-Févr./37 avec vous et seul. Et c'est ici que je reviens, en vous cablant "ACCEPTE EN PRINCIPE," à cette question tant de fois discutée par nous et résumée dans la "conclusion" de ma lettre à vous du 16 nov. dernier. Je consentirai à une tournée aus E.-U. en janv.-févr.(-mars à la rigueur) 1937 si cette tournée pourra m'offrir des garanties suffisantes morales et matérielles. Cette saison de mon point de vue ne me donnait malheureusement rien de tout cela: Perséphone si brillamment lancée par moi l'année dernière à Boston fut rendu aux autres (Philadelphia et N-Y) qui devaient la diriger dans ma présence, les programmes que j'avais à diriger n'étaient pas établis ce qui veut dire en [verso:] bon français – rien de nouveau et interessant dans mes programmes symphoniques, toujours la même chose: l'Oiseau et Pétrouchka! – ça c'est pour le moral. Et pour le côté matériel vous comprenez vous-même qu'une somme de quatre mille dolars sur laquel selon vous je pouvais compter comme bénéfice de trois mois de travail ne se présente pas à mes yeux comme un avantage suffisant pour me décider à abandonner tout: mon travail de composition, ma famille et tout ce qui m'est cher. Le succès relatif moral et matériel de ma dernière tournée me faisait espérer, avec la reprise des affaires chez vous, quelque chose de bien plus interessant. Certainement les circonstances malencontreuses dans lesquelles c'est trouvé Merovitch et son Management sont en majeure partie la cause mais je ne pense pas que même si les conditions matérielles de Merovitch étaient interessantes que les questions morales seraient changées à mon avantage. Mais dans tous les cas une garantie de quatre mille dolars pour trois mois (ce que vous m'offriez avec Kavenoki) ne saurait aucunement servir comme base acceptable de garantie pour nos projets de l'année prochaine. Pour que ces projets deviennent une réalité il faut que celui qui s'occupera de ma tournée puisse vraiment me trouver une série d'engagements valables, présentants pour moi des avantages aussi bien matériels que morals. Autrement dit les uns sans les autres (et vous savez mieux que personnes ce que je désire) ne comptent pas comme valables pour moi.

Chez nous tout est calme pour le moment; fin janv. ma femme va rejoindre la montagne (probablement en Suisse) pour se fortifier définitivement (j'espère). Mars – c'est l'Espagne pour moi avec Nini et un concert en Angleterre aussi avec lui. Avril-Mai probablement l'Argentine (aussi avec Nini).

Je serai tellement heureux d'avoir de vos nouvelles qu'obstinément vous ne voulez pas me donner. Par discrétion je ne vous demande pas la cause et vous embrasse simplement de tout coeur.

[signed:] Votre Igor Feodorovich

[marginalia on recto (beginning at left):]

J'attends toujours une réponse à mes lettres: une – le recommendation de Balanchine au Metropolitan, pour laquelle le maître de ballet n'pas jugé necessaire de me remercier, malgré que c'était lui qui ne l'avait demandé (par Païchadze), une autre, tout je vous telegraphiais au sujet de la commande d'un ballet (aussi par Païchadze) [upper margin:] une dernière lettre exige également une reponse car c'est aussi Balanchine qui me demande c'est de lui dire ce que j'en pense. Je n'ai rien parlé du coté particuliere, j'ai seulement demandé (en donnant mon acceptance de principe) qu'on entre en pourparlers avec moi si l'on veut avoir le ballet l'automne 1936. Ma lettre [right margin:] est partie fin novembre – aucune réponse! C'est désolant. Gardez tout ça pour vous et agissez discrètement si agir on peut. Je ne sais rien, rien ce qui se passe et le temps passe aussi.

I am still waiting for a reply to my letters: the one – a recommendation of Balanchine for the Metropolitan [Opera], for which the ballet master [Balanchine] did not [even] think it necessary to thank me, even though it was he who asked me for it (through [Gavryil] Païchadze [in Paris]); the other [letter] about which I telegraphed you [is] on the subject of the commission of a ballet (also through Païchadze); this second letter also requires a reply because it is also Balanchine who asked me to tell him what I think of it. I said nothing of the business side, I simply asked (while giving my acceptance in principle) that they should enter into negotiations with me if they want to have the ballet in the autumn of 1936. My letter left [here] in November [1935] – no reply! It is distressing. Keep all this to your self and act discreetly if one can [so] act. I can see nothing, nothing happening, and time is passing also.)

[marginalia on verso (at left):]

Ces Messieurs de la Schola Cantorum m'envient un cable pour me demander de leur écrire un article de 200 mots pour la première de Perséphone que je voulais tellement moi faire à N.Y. Même 200 dolars ne me décidera pas à leur faire cet article et je laisse leur cable sans réponse.

These gentlemen from the Schola Cantorum sent me a cable asking me to write them an article of 200 words for the premiere of *Perséphone*, which

I really wanted to do [i.e., conduct] myself in New York. Even 200 dollars could not persuade me to write this article and I have not responded to their cable.

[marginalia on verso (at right):]

Quand arrive Beveridge?
When does [pianist Webster] arrive?

Acquisition: H. Colin Slim in Berkeley, CA, on 10 October 2012 from J. & J. Lubrano Music Antiquarians, Lloyd Harbor, NY. Donated by Professor Slim in July 2016. *Provenance*: Estate of Samuel Dushkin (1891–1976), and probably thereafter from the estate of his late wife, Louise (née Rorimer). Only the typed portion of the letter is translated in SSC, vol. 2, pp. 305–6 (although with one wrong date and occasional inaccuracies).

Commentary

The typed portion of Stravinsky's letter exemplifies the challenges, difficulties, and disappointments he experienced in planning transatlantic tours for 1936 and 1937 from France to the United States and return. His marginalia reveal him attempting to control negotiations for a new ballet score, *Jeu de cartes* (1935–36), already begun. In the event, he concertized with his son in 1936 in South America, and in 1937 with Dushkin in the USA and that year – for a first time – in Canada.

Works Consulted

Joseph, Charles M. *Stravinsky's Ballets*. New Haven and London: Yale University Press, 2011. pp. 144–45.
SSC. vol. 2. pp. 305–6 (a translation from Stravinsky's carbon copy of his typed letter, and thus lacking all his marginalia).
SSE. pp. 40–41.

43i   (1936). Printed twelve-page program, 23.2 × 15.9 cm, for a concert on 2 May 1936 at the Teatro Colón, Buenos Aires. Stravinsky initialled his photograph in ink on p. 1 of the program; his son Soulima signed his photograph on p. 10, facing an (unsigned) photograph, p. 11, of choreographer Bronislava Nijinska (1891–1972).

Acquisition: H. Colin Slim in Berkeley, CA, in September 2016 from J. & J. Lubrano Music Antiquarians, Syosset, NY, *The Paul J. Jackson Opera Collection,* part VII: R–S (September 2016), lot 760. Donated by Professor Slim in June 2017.
Provenance: Paul J. Jackson, who kindly informed Professor Slim (letter of 4 October 2016) that he acquired this program from La Scala Autographs, Pennington, NJ, on 3 September 1991.

Commentary
Stravinsky and his son performed several times – separately and together – at the Teatro Colón during their concert tour to South America in May 1936. At this all-Stravinsky concert on 2 May, Soulima played four-hands with his father and was also soloist in his father's *Capriccio* for piano and orchestra (1929), conducted by the composer. For another example of Soulima's signature, where he again played *Capriccio* led by his father, see Entry 61.

Works Consulted
Levitz, Tamara. "Igor the Angeleno: The Mexican Connection." *Stravinsky and His World*. Edited by Tamara Levitz. Princeton and Oxford: Princeton University Press, 2013. pp. 153–62.
Slim, H. Colin. "A Stravinsky Holograph in 1936 for Juan José Castro in Buenos Aires: 'maître impeccable de la baguette'." *Music Observed: Studies in Memory of William C. Holmes*. Edited by Colleen Reardon and Susan Parisi. Warren, MI: Harmonie Park Press, 2004. pp. 447–58.
SSE. pp. 42–49.

47i (1937). Autograph, unstamped postcard, 9 × 14 cm, signed 25 March 1937, but lacking its mailing envelope. On its obverse a colour image depicts "ALBUQUERQUE, NEW MEXICO, FROM THE AIR." A message in French mentioning [Boris] Morros (1891–1963), then director of Paramount's Music Department, is to "Chère amie," i.e., Dagmar Godowsky (1897–1975), former silent movie actress and daughter of the celebrated pianist Leopold Godowsky (1870–1938):

Dear lady-friend: San Francisco 25 III 37
A thousand best regards from your sincerely devoted I. Stravinsky.
Morros will come to New York on 14 or 15 April with a libretto that
is in the process of being prepared for me in Hollywood. If it suits me,
we will conclude this matter which I hope will be profitable for me.

Acquisition: H. Colin Slim, in Berkeley, CA, on 12 November 2004 from J. & J.
Lubrano, Lloyd Harbor, NY, lot 157. Donated by Professor Slim in July 2012.
Provenance: Probably from Christie's sale, *Illuminated Manuscripts, Illustrated Books,
Autograph Letters and Music* (London: 29 June 1994), pp. 148–49 (lot 124).

Commentary
The message side of the postcard is reproduced (slightly enlarged) and discussed
in Slim, "Chère amie," cited below.

Works Consulted
Slim, H. Colin. "Chère amie: The Mystery of the Unstamped Postcard." *Sleuthing
the Muse: Essays in Honor of William F. Prizer*. Edited by Kristine K. Forney and
Jeremy L. Smith. Hillsdale, NY: Pendragon Press, 2012. pp. 329–48 (including the
original French).

66i (1939?). Large undated autograph signature: "Igor Strawinsky" in black ink, on an
irregularly sheared rectangle of paper: 7.3 cm (left side) and 8 cm (right side) ×
20.3 cm (top and bottom). This slightly uneven rectangle was cut from the upper
portion of a page of medium brown notepaper, watermarked with eight vertical
stripes. The sales cataloguer for J. & J. Lubrano dated **66i** as "c. 1939." Careless
shearing cropped part of the long (curling) tail of the last letter of Stravinsky's
surname. The other side of this rectangle bears handwritten observations in a
black ink (shared?) by two persons, one of whom is Mary Rose Bradford, née
Himler (c. 1908–post 1963). The other person is an unidentified (female?) friend
of Mrs. Bradford, [M?....lle?] Powers, whose first name of eight letters (perhaps
Michelle? Maybelle? Marianne?) is now unverifiable owing to the angle at which
the paper was cut.

Acquisition: H. Colin Slim in Berkeley, CA, on 22 September 2016 from J. & J. Lubrano Music Antiquarians, Syosset, NY, *The Paul J. Jackson Opera Collection*, part VII: R–S (September 2016), lot 759. Donated by Professor Slim in June 2017. *Provenance*: Paul J. Jackson, who kindly informed Professor Slim (letter of 4 October 2016) that he had acquired lot 759 at an auction, 13 September 1994, from Alexander Autographs, a firm variously located in Connecticut.

Commentary

On the recto of this irregularly sized snippet of paper appears in black ink in one hand: "Lopez – Tops in dance bands / Lopez – Double check tops in band leaders / Come back soon, Lopez! / [signed:] Mary Rose Bradford / November 1939 / New Orleans." Below and slightly to the left, in a different hand (but probably in the same black ink) is: "I've got to thank Mary Rose / for finally meeting you – / [Michelle? Maybelle? Marianne?] Powers." (The missing lower portions of the letters from Powers's first name make its identification uncertain.) Surely "meeting you" means Vincent Lopez (1895–1975), not Stravinsky.

Mary Rose Bradford (née Himler) – second wife of the Southern novelist Roark Bradford (1896–1948), whom she married in the 1930s – was a musician herself. While in college, c. 1925–27, she played pipe organ at a movie-vaudeville house in Indianapolis.

The "c. 1939" date assigned by J. & J. Lubrano may well be correct: Lopez and his band performed in New Orleans in mid-February 1939. Mrs. Bradford reported to *Life* that Lopez had dined in February 1938 at her house in the French Quarter, where he played her Mason & Hamlin piano. Stravinsky was not in New Orleans in 1938 or 1939, but he perhaps docked there briefly in mid-May 1940, and was certainly there 10–11 March 1946, 10 February 1950, 1–2 February 1955 (Hotel St. Charles), and 3 December 1955 (Sunset Hotel). Whether or not he met Lopez (or even Mrs. Bradford) during any of these visits to New Orleans is unknown.

Lopez had visited the Bradfords in New Orleans in mid-February 1938 during an engagement there with his band at the Tulane Room in the Jung Hotel, and he performed there again with his band a year later. He probably received Entry **66i** (personally? by mail?) from his hostess fan and her friend in November 1939, or soon thereafter. A photograph of mid-December 1939 depicts Lopez dining with Stravinsky and Pierre Monteux in San Francisco, the only time that Lopez and Stravinsky are known to have met. Neither Lopez nor

Stravinsky looks as if he is enjoying the company of the other. (Only Monteux seems to be having a good time.) At some point in Lopez's travels – perhaps that very December in San Francisco – and lacking any other piece of paper, he might have sought Stravinsky's signature on **66i**. An avid autograph collector, Lopez would not have mutilated Stravinsky's signature. Some other collector or a dealer did so by cutting the paper to its present slightly irregular dimensions.

When in San Francisco, did Stravinsky and Lopez discuss swing? There is no evidence that Stravinsky, who, late in 1940, professed enjoying "swings," knew of Lopez's forecast in 1938 that the genre was doomed to extinction by 1944.

Beyond being excellent pianists, Lopez and Stravinsky had little in common. Both men, however, were pilloried for arranging *The Star-Spangled Banner* (the former in 1938, the latter in 1941–42, and especially in 1944).

Works Consulted

Bradford, Mary Rose. "Letter to the Editor." *Life* 4 (14 March 1938): 2.

–. "My Short Happy Life in the Theater." *The Atlantic* 211, no. 8 (March 1963): 136–38.

Cogswell, Michael. "Lopez, Vincent." *American National Biography*. vol. XIII. New York: Oxford University Press, 1999, pp. 909–10.

Cox, Jim. *Musicmakers of Network Radio: 24 Entertainers 1926–1962*. Jefferson, NC, and London: McFarland, 2012. pp. 210–24 (especially on Lopez's charm for women).

Dehmel, Victor. "Lopez Forecasts 'Swing' to Endure for 6 More Years." *[New Orleans] Times-Picayune* (16 February 1938): 22 (with his photograph at the piano).

Lopez, Vincent. *Lopez Speaking: An Autobiography*. New York: Citadel, 1960. pp. 298–300, 306, 318, 338.

Simms, L. Moody, Jr. "Bradford, Roark Whitney Wickliff (1886–1948)." *American National Biography*. New York: Oxford University Press, 1999. III, 361.

Slim, H. Colin. "Stravinsky's Four Star-Spangled Banners and His 1941 Christmas Card." *The Musical Quarterly* 89, nos. 2–3 (Summer–Fall 2006): 347.

SP&D. p. 644 (n. 28).

SSC. vol. 2. pl. 10 (cropped at right side?).

SSE. pp. 124, 601 (n. 3).

72i (1940). Autographed cropped photograph – but in reverse – of Stravinsky taken by George Hoyningen-Huene at Paris on 16 November 1934, 10.8 × 16 cm, mounted on same-sized heavy cardboard. Inscribed, probably September 1940, upper left and middle right in French in black ink in the background, for Mrs. Marcus Koshland, San Francisco:

> Pour Madame
> Marcus
> Koshland
> son admirateur
> Igor Strawinsky
> 1940

Acquisition: Gratis in 2016 from a Berkeley collector. Donated by Professor Slim in July 2016. *Provenance*: Private collection, San Francisco. Jean Gray Hargrove Music Library, Berkeley, deaccessioned in 2015.

Commentary

The photograph is a slightly cropped image – in reverse – of a 1934 Hoyningen-Huene photograph. After Stravinsky's Hollywood Bowl concert, 30 August 1940, the Stravinskys drove north for a brief vacation to San Francisco, where, on 8 September, they stayed with Mrs. Marcus S. Koshland, and returned to Hollywood five days later. Among musicians, Mrs. Koshland was known to have the best chef in San Francisco! Presumably Stravinsky inscribed this photograph during their visit, or sent it to her upon returning to Hollywood.

Works Consulted

Adaskin, Harry. *A Fiddler's World: Memoirs to 1938.* Vancouver, BC: November House, 1977. p. 260.

Ewing, William A. *The Photographic Art of Hoyningen-Huene.* London: Thames and Hudson, 1986. p. 242 (pl. 96, incorrectly dated by Ewing as 1927).

Lubrano, J. & J. *Catalogue 61.* Lloyd Harbor, NY: 2004, lot 178 (an [unreversed] exemplar signed in 1941 and illustrated – its size not furnished – but described as a "postcard photograph").

Strawinsky, Sein Nachlass. Sein Bild [including a] *Katalog der ausgestellten Bildnisse und Entwürfe für die Ausstattung seiner Bühnenwerke.* Basel: Kunstmuseum und Paul Sacher Stiftung, 1984. pp. 126–[27], upper image.

75i

(1941). *THE / STAR-SPANGLED / BANNER / Words by / FRANCIS SCOTT KEY / Music by / JOHN STAFFORD SMITH / Harmonized and Orchestrated by / IGOR STRAWINSKY*, full score, four unnumbered pages, 30.9 × 23.5 cm, enclosed in same-sized wrapper (New York: Mercury Music Corporation, 1941) – a reissue, lacking red and blue lettering on cover and any information about the premiere – signed by Murray Adaskin (1906–2002).

Acquisition: Kind donation by Dorothea Adaskin in fall–winter 2002; date acquired by her husband is unknown.

Provenance: Murray Adaskin, on whom see below, Entry **86i** (1950).

Commentary

In October 1941, Stravinsky sent his autograph full score of his arrangement of the US national anthem for chorus and symphony orchestra, finished by 4 July – together with his handwritten preface – to President Franklin D. Roosevelt. Both autograph and preface are in the Library of Congress. In the present full score, **75i**, Mercury printed Stravinsky's preface, not found in his reduction for piano and chorus, about which, see Entry 75.

Copies of the piano-vocal and full orchestral scores now in the Jean Gray Hargrove Music Library at the University of California, Berkeley, both previously owned by the late Professor Charles C. Cushing (on whom see Entry 101), were dated in ink by Cushing on their front covers: "Dec. 1941" and "January 1942," respectively. The latter's full score, 32.9 × 23.7 cm, is not only slightly larger than Adaskin's exemplar, **75i**, but Cushing's cream-coloured front cover is printed in red and dark blue. As in Adaskin's exemplar, Stravinsky's facsimile dedication is on a first (unnumbered) recto page, facing the verso of the front cover. Unlike Adaskin's exemplar, however, Cushing's exemplar has printed on the verso of its rear cover: "This composition was first performed at the Embassy Auditorium in Los Angeles, California on October 14th, 1941 by the Works Projects Administration's Symphony Orchestra (Dr. Karl Wecker, State Supervisor) and Negro Chorus assisted by Los Angeles Oratorio Society, James Sample conducting."

Works Consulted

Lerma, Dominique-René de. *Igor Fedorovitch Stravinsky, 1882–1971: A Practical Guide to Publications of His Music.* Kent, OH: Kent State University Press, 1974. p. 102 (no. Z15).

Slim, H. Colin. *Annotated Catalogue.* Entry 75.

–. "Stravinsky's Four Star-Spangled Banners and His 1941 Christmas Card." *The Musical Quarterly* 89, nos. 2–3 (Summer–Fall 2006): 321–447.

79i

(1944). Typed single-page letter, 28 × 21.5 cm, in French, 5 January 1944, with autograph marginal annotations in pencil and ink, to Walter de Bourg, Esq., Légation de Suisse, Washington, DC, and signed "Igor Strawinsky." Except for his handwritten additions, Stravinsky's letter lacks all French accents, presumably unavailable on his typewriter:

1260 N. Wetherly Drive,
Hollywood, 46, Cal
5 January, 1944.

Cher Monsieur de Bourg,

C'etais une grande emotion pour nous, cette lettre de mon fils
que vous avez eu la gentillesse de me faire parvenir. Je vous en remercie
tres cordialement.

Je profite de cette occasion pour lui donner de mon cote de nos
nouvelles que vous avez eu la bonte de bien vouloir lui transmettre.

Voici donc le message:

1) Recu sa lettre du 2 novembre,★ recu egalement son cable du
30 decembre. [★in pencil:] la seule reçue depuis sa lettre du 25 Janv./43

2) Je m'en vais pour une tournee de concerts et serai de retour
– fin janvier.

3) J'ai fais en plusieurs reprises (depuis le mois d'octobre) la demande
a la Swiss Bank Corporation de New York de remettre a mon fils
Theodore, selon la license qui m'etait accordee, des dollars
et non des francs suisses. Jusqu'ici je n'a ai pas pu avoir satisfaction
pour des raisons qui ne me sont pas connues, c'est pour j'ai donne
l'ordre d'arreter ces envois (le cours des francs libres devenant une
vraie ruine). Cependant mes demarches continuent et je ne perds
pas l'espoir de lui obtenir l'envoi en dollars et non en fr. suisses.

4) Par contre je viens d'obtenir pour ma belle fille Denise une
license pour des envois mensuels de $100 et le premier envoi au
cours officiel est effectue le 28 dec. dernier.

5) Lorsque je serai de retour je vais tacher d'agir par la Croix
Rouge pour aider ma fille malade ou du moins faire savoir a son
sanatorium que je me porte garant des depenses que necessite son
etat de sante.

6) Notre sante est bonne. Nous attendons enxieusement
de leurs nouvelles de l'etat de sante de ma fille malade et de
tous les autres. J'espere pouvoir ecrire denouveau a mon retour.

Je veux croire que je n'abuse pas trop de votre gentillesse
et c'est dans cet espoir que je vous prie, cher Monsieur de Bourg,
de trouver ici l'expression de mes sentiments devoues et reconnaissants.

[signed:] Igor Strawinsky

Walter de Bourg, Esq.
Legation de Suisse
Washington, D.C.

[below, left, in ink in Stravinsky's hand:]
    P.S. L'adresse actuelle de / mon fils Thédore est: / 40, rue du Marché, Genève.
[below, right, in ink in Stravinsky's hand:]
    x) La seule reçue depuis / sa lettre du 25 Janv./43

                                    1260 N. Wetherly Drive,
                                    Hollywood, 46, Cal.
                                    5 January, 1944.

Dear Monsieur de Bourg:
    We were deeply moved by my son's [Theodore's] letter that you
so kindly passed on to me. I thank you very much. I should like to use
this occasion to send him word from me about us which you would be
so good as to send on to him.
    So here is the message:
    1) Received his letter of 2 November,★ [pencilled here and in ink,
bottom right of page:] "the only one received since his letter of Jan
25.43" as well as the one of 30 December [1943.]
    2) I am leaving for concert tours and will be back at the end of January.
    3) I have requested several times (since October [1943]) that the Swiss
Bank Corporation of New York send my son Theodore dollars instead of
Swiss francs, as granted by the license I obtained. Since my request has
not been honored for reasons unknown to me, I have ordered the
transfers be stopped (the free francs rate becoming an utter disaster).
However, I am still working on it, and I have not lost hope that I can
arrange a transfer of dollars for him, and not in Swiss fr.
    4) On the other hand, I just obtained a license to send monthly
payments of $100 for my daughter-in-law, Denise, and the first transfer
at the official rate went out on Dec. 29.
    5) When I return, I shall try to arrange help through the Red Cross
for my sick daughter [Milène], or at least to let her [tuberculosis]

sanatorium [at Sancellemoz] know that I am good for any expenses that her state of health necessitates.

6) We are in good health. We are awaiting anxiously to hear news about our sick daughter's state of health and about everybody else. I expect to write again after my return.

I hope I am not taking too much advantage of your kindness, dear Monsieur de Bourg, and it is with that hope that I send you most sincere best wishes and gratitude.

[Signed] Igor Strawinsky

Walter de Bourg, Esq.
Legation de Suisse,
Washington, D.C.

Acquisition: H. Colin Slim in Berkeley, CA, from Lion Heart Autographs, Inc., New York, on 7 May 2015. Donated by Professor Slim in July 2016.
Provenance: Unknown, perhaps the estate of Walter de Bourg.

Commentary

Entry **79i** is to be considered in light of Stravinsky's earlier statement on [18?] October 1941 to his "elderly" student Earnest Andersson (1878–1943) about "needing to send about 50 [dollars] per month to his daughter [Milène] who is in a [tuberculosis] sanatorium in unoccupied France," cited in Slim, "Lessons with Stravinsky," and Stravinsky's letter to de Bourg of 28 October 1944, cited in Slim, *Annotated Catalogue*, and also in light of an inscribed photograph: "Pour Monsieur / Walter de Bourg / avec tous mes / voeux d'un bon / et heureux / retour en Suisse / I Strawinsky / Hollywood, / Nov.1944 " as described in *Autographen Katalog* 916 (Basel: Erasmushaus, May 2003), pp. 86–87 (lot 191).

Works Consulted

Slim, H. Colin. *Annotated Catalogue*. Entry 82.
—. "Lessons with Stravinsky: The Notebook of Earnest Andersson (1878–1943)."
      JAMS 62, no. 2 (Summer 2009): 400 ([18?] October 1941).

82i (1944). Autographed – now empty – large brown envelope, 21.5 × 26.7 cm, (its postage stamps cut away) of 16 November 1944. At upper left, the composer wrote in black ink: "from Igor Strawinsky / 1260 N. Wetherly Dr. / Hollywood 46, Calif. SPECIAL / DELIVERY," this latter below a printed red, white, and blue sticker, "VIA AIR MAIL." He addressed this envelope: "to Walter de Bourg, Esq. / Legation of Switzerland / 2900 Cathedral Avenue, N.W. / Washington, D.C." and below, left, he wrote: "REGISTERED." The envelope is stamped by the post office: "VIA AIR MAIL / Special Delivery" and "REGISTERED / 251628."

The envelope's reverse side is circle-stamped seven times in purple ink: "WEST, CALIF. / NOV / 15 / 1944," once as: "WASHINGTON, D.C. / 17 / NOV / 1944," and once in black ink: "WASHINGTON DC / STATE DEPT NO. 1."

Acquisition: H. Colin Slim in Berkeley, CA, on 14 September 2016 from J. & J. Lubrano Music Antiquarians, Syosset, NY, *The Paul J. Jackson Opera Collection*, part VII: R–S (September 2016), lot 758 (item 23365). Donated by Professor Slim in June 2017.

This envelope is accompanied by two excerpts from two different – unidentified, but perhaps British – auction catalogues, plus notations made on them by Mr. Jackson, probably in late February 1990. Each of these auction catalogues describes one signed and typed Stravinsky letter in French sent to de Bourg from Hollywood: lot 249 of 16 September 1944, and lot 252 of 22 October 1944, respectively, neither traceable.

Provenance: Paul J. Jackson, who kindly informed Professor Slim (letter of 4 October 2016) that he had purchased this envelope, **82i**, on 15 February 1990 from the autograph dealer Robert F. Batchelder, Ambler, PA.

Commentary

The size of the envelope suggests that it could have contained a musical score. If so, this score was probably destined for Théodore Stravinsky in Switzerland, rather than for his son Soulima, then in occupied France.

Works Consulted

Slim, H. Colin. *Annotated Catalogue*. Entry 82.

83i (1945–46). *IGOR STRAVINSKY / PETROUSHKA / A BURLESQUE IN FOUR SCENES*, 24.5 × 16 cm (London: Boosey & Hawkes, [1945]), 152 pp., [from the rear wrapper:] "Hawkes Pocket Scores, no. 574." Entry **83i** is a reprint of Serge Koussevitzky's edition (Berlin: Russischer Musikverlag, 1912 [later, Paris: Édition Russe]). **83i**'s outer cover page is signed, upper right, in black ink: "Igor Stravinsky." His autograph markings for revisions appear on seventy-four pages in ink, in pencil, and in reds, blues, and greens. "PETROUSHKA" – lettered in upper case in black ink on the spine – is probably also in Stravinsky's hand, because its first six and last three letters are spaced similarly to the initial six and final three of "PETROUCHKA" [*sic*] lettered in ink on the spine of his autograph score in his library, formerly at 1218 North Wetherly, Hollywood. A small sticker, "BROUDE BROS. / Music / NEW YORK," is affixed to the title page of Entry **83i**.

Acquisition: H. Colin Slim in Berkeley, CA, on 9 December 2015 – bidding courtesy Edward C. Hirschland, Chicago, at Bonhams' auction in New York. Donated by Professor Slim in June 2017.
Provenance: Said by its previous (and anonymous) owner (not Harry E. Gould, see below) to have been purchased, c. 2005, from a Los Angeles dealer. How it escaped Stravinsky's possession remains unknown.

Commentary

Stravinsky had no copy of the original 1912 edition at hand – his copy was in Europe and still unavailable – when he began his revision in 1945. Thus, he was obliged to obtain and to work from Entry **83i**, this Boosey & Hawkes reprinted edition. The "BROUDE BROS." sticker might well suggest that Stravinsky bought **83i** in New York – he was there all January and most of February 1945. However, Ronald Broude kindly informed me (22 June 2016) that his firm has no trace of Stravinsky's purchase of **83i** (unlike a different item published by Boosey & Hawkes and cited in the 2002 *Annotated Catalogue*, Entry 108, an item also stocked by Broude Bros.). Robert Craft's essay in 1982 about revisions to *Petrushka* (though not clarifying whether or not Craft knew about Entry **83i**) reveals that Stravinsky sketched variants on his 1260 North Wetherly Drive notepaper for "Petrushka / Magician" (at rehearsal 130), variants that ultimately he did not fully adopt in his revised version.

Stravinsky's above-cited markings appear on seventy-four of Entry **83i**'s pages, i.e., 6–11, 13–14, 16–17, 22–27, 29, 37, 44, 53–57, 73, 78–83, 85–87, 89–91, 97, 100–1, 103–4, 107, 110, 113–18, 123–32, 135, 137, 139–48, and 150–52. These markings were for his forthcoming revision of his ballet score, issued subsequently as: *PETROUCHKA / Burlesque in Four Scenes / Full Score / revised 1947 version… copyright 1948*, 32.5 × 26 cm, B. & H. 16236, London: Boosey & Hawkes (1948), 172 pp. (B. & H. reprinted this revised edition in 1965.) Application for copyright was received by the US Copyright Office on 17 January 1947. The 1948 revised edition was then duplicated by an ensuing and smaller-sized "Pocket Score," 18.5 × 13.5 cm, B. & H. 639, London: Boosey & Hawkes (April 1950), entailing several (non-musical) typographical divergences.

A sole non-autograph marking: "Side 2," added in pencil by a previous owner, appears on p. 92, upper left, of Entry **83i** at the beginning of the fourth tableau. (This marking is not in Robert Craft's hand.) Because most recordings take about twenty minutes for the first three tableaux, the annotation must refer to some recording of *Petrushka* – not necessarily conducted by Stravinsky – made during the LP era from c. 1948 (predating the advent of compact discs).

With its orchestral score composed 1910–11, the ballet was first staged on 13 June 1911 in Paris, Vaslav Nijinsky in the title role, Pierre Monteux leading the orchestra. The first edition of its score was printed at Berlin by Serge Koussevitzky's Russischer Musikverlag [Édition Russe] in 1912. Autograph corrections in red ink and blue and red pencil made in 1911 are in the second proofs of the orchestra score, now in Paris, Bibliothèque Nationale. As early as June 1914, Stravinsky's revisions for *Petrushka* were in proofs but never published, owing to World War I.

Rehearsing *Petrushka* late in February 1935 with the Los Angeles Philharmonic, Stravinsky complained about misplaced accidentals in the orchestra parts. At Christmas 1939, he told Dorothy McQuoid in Los Angeles that her score, pirated by Kalmus in 1933, was faulty (see Entry 68). By late November 1945, he had revised the "first part." These revisions, contracted in January 1946 by Boosey & Hawkes and completed mid-October that year, were scored for a slightly reduced orchestra. On 7 February 1947, Stravinsky wrote to a Boosey & Hawkes representative in New York that he was sending him "the full orchestra score (157 black negative pages) of the new *Petrushka* orchestra version which Mr. Hawkes [in London] also requested."

Craft observed that "many of the 1947 [*sic*] revisions actually date from 1912." Hamm rightly called the *Petrushka* of 1911 and of 1947 "two rather different pieces." Walsh deemed the result a "radical retexturing," Taruskin finding it "a considerable impoverishment."

Both Stravinsky manuscripts for his 1911 score of *Petrushka* and for his 1945–46 revision of it are in the Morgan Library, New York (deposits from the Robert Owen Lehman Collection). The Juilliard School of Music holds a forty-six-page sketchbook, dated 29 September 1910, comprising Tableaux I–III. Four pages of autograph sketches and a photocopy of the revised autograph full score are in the Library of Congress.

In Entry **83i**, the nature of Stravinsky's markings suggests his preliminary assessment of a coming – and onerous – task of revision. He corrects previous printing errors, adds beams, and pencils in suggestions for changes, virtually all of which would appear in the new Boosey & Hawkes 1948 edition, no. 16236, *Petrouchka… revised 1947 version*, its final page signed: "I. Strawinsky. Hollywood, 1946."

Bibliographical assistance was kindly provided by John Shepard, Jean Gray Hargrove Music Library at University of California, Berkeley; George Boziwick, Chief of the Music Division, New York Public Library; and Lisa Shiota, Music Division, Library of Congress.

Acquisition and donation of Entry **83i** complement the nine *Petrushka* items previously given by Professor Slim to UBC. They span more than a half-century: Entries 1 (1911), 6 and 7 (both 1914), 8 and 9 (both 1915), 34 (1926), 49 (1937), 68 (1939), **83i** (1946), and 119 (1967). Entry 1 (22 May 1911) in the UBC collection even precedes *Petrushka*'s premiere by three weeks.

Works Consulted

Bonhams. *Fine Books and Manuscripts Including the Autograph Collection of Harry E. Gould, Jr.* New York: 9 December 2015, lot 159 (with two illustrations).

Boys, Henry. "Note on the New Petrouchka." *Tempo* (Summer 1948): 15–18.

Craft, Robert. *A Stravinsky Scrapbook 1940–1971.* London: Thames and Hudson, 1983. p. 21 (pl. 44), p. 100 (pl. 206); both plates illustrate Craft's handwriting.

Ettl, Helga. *Petruschka.* Stuttgart: Klett, 1968. pp. 28, 86–88, n. 26.

Evans, Edwin. *Stravinsky: The Fire-Bird and Petrushka.* London: Oxford University Press, 1933.

Hamm, Charles, ed. *Igor Stravinsky: Petrushka: An Authoritative Score of the Original Version, Backgrounds, Analysis, Essays, Views, and Comments.* New York: W.W. Norton, 1967. p. 19.

Joseph, Charles M. "Stravinsky Manuscripts in the Library of Congress and the

Pierpont Morgan Library." *The Journal of Musicology* 1, no. 3 (July 1982): 337 (no. 8).

–. *Stravinsky's Ballets*. New Haven and London: Yale University Press, 2011. pp. 48–72, 255–56 (n. 5).

Lerma, Dominique-René de. *Igor Fedorovitch Stravinsky, 1882–1971: A Practical Guide to Publications of His Music*. Kent, OH: Kent State University Press, 1974. p. 60 (nos. P15 [6] and P16 [1]).

Lesure, François, ed. *Igor Stravinsky: La carrière européenne*. Paris: Musée d'art moderne, 1980. p. 29 (no. 77).

Los Angeles Illustrated Daily News. 21 February 1935: 4.

Newman, Arnold, and Robert Craft. Foreword by Francis Steegmuller. *Bravo Stravinsky*. Cleveland, OH, and New York: World Publishing Company, 1967. Final unnumbered verso page: a volume lettered at far left, "original 1944 [*sic*] version…"

Rozhdestvensky, G. "On the Two Editions of Igor Stravinsky's Ballet *Petrushka*." *I.F. Stravinsky: Stat'i i materiali*. Edited by L.S. Dyachkova and B.M. Yarustovsky. Moscow: Sovetskiy Kompozitor, 1973. pp. 109–43.

Slim, H. Colin. *Annotated Catalogue*. Entries 1, 6 ("partition d'orch."), pp. 7, 9, 34, 49, 68, 108, 119.

SE&D. p. 159 (item 2).

SP&D. pp. 68, 85–86 (31 March 1912), 377–78, 610 (n. 118).

SP&RK. vol. 1. pp. 495–96 (no. 23).

SSC. vol. 1. pp. 391–97 (pl. on p. 394); vol. 2. p. 429 (n. 13); vol. 3. pp. 313, 318, 322, 325, 327–28, 333, 337.

SSE. pp. 190–91, 194–95, 207–8.

Stephan, Rudolf. "Vom alten und vom neuen Petruschka." *Neue Zeitschrift für Musik* 123, no. 6 (June 1962): 255–61.

Stuart, Philip. "Petrushka." *Igor Stravinsky – The Composer in the Recording Studio: A Comprehensive Discography*. Westport, CT: Greenwood Press, 1991. p. 89.

Taruskin, Richard. *Stravinsky and the Russian Traditions*. Berkeley and Los Angeles: University of California Press, 1996. p. 986 (n. 2).

–. *Russian Music at Home and Abroad: New Essays*. Oakland: University of California Press, 2016. p. 540 (index: *Petrushka*).

Wachtel, Andrew, ed. *Petrushka: Sources and Contents*. Evanston, IL: Northwestern University Press, 1998.

Walsh, Stephen. "Apollo in the Marketplace: Stravinsky and His Manuscripts." *Settling New Scores: Music Manuscripts from the Paul Sacher Foundation*. Edited by Felix

Meyer. Mainz: Schott, for the Paul Sacher Foundation, Basel, 1998. pp. 66–67 (erroneously locating the 1911 MS score of *Petrushka* at the Library of Congress).

White, Eric Walter. *Stravinsky: The Composer and His Works*, 2nd ed. Berkeley and Los Angeles: University of California Press, 1979; repr. 1984. pp. 37, 194 (locating the 1911 *Petrushka* autograph in New York with Boosey & Hawkes), 196–97, 201–3, 617 (no. 88).

Yuzefovich, Victor. "Chronicle of a Non-Friendship: Letters of Stravinsky and Koussevitzky." *The Musical Quarterly* 86, no. 4 (Winter 2002): 821 (no. 85, Stravinsky's letter of 20 November 1945: "Petrouchka, first part [in my new orchestration]"), 880 (letter 8, n. 2).

84i (1946). Autograph signed letter, 17.5 × 13.5 cm, 25 September 1946, in Russian (excepting dates, cities, and "concert tours"), lacking its envelope and addressee. The letter's single fold suggests that it was mailed to such unidentified Russian-speaking "Dear friends" as George Balanchine (1904–83), or Alexei Haieff (1914–94), or Lucia Davidova, but perhaps not to Nicolas Nabokov (1903–78), then in Europe, returning to the USA in January 1947:

> Hollywood
> Sept 25
> 1946

> Dear friends,
> What should we do? As usual I'll be doing the concert tours during December and January. From the 12th★) until Christmas I'll be in New York where I'll be returning later (from the 12th until 19th of January again in N–Y). After that only on 5th of February in Los Angeles. I'm waiting for your answer.
>
> Yours,
> ★) December   I. Stravinsky.

Acquisition: H. Colin Slim in Berkeley, CA, on 12 November 2004, from J. & J. Lubrano Music Antiquarians. Donated by Professor Slim in July 2012; translation by Richard Taruskin.
Provenance: Unknown.

Commentary

That the addressee was *not* Nabokov might seem likely because the trustees of his papers at New Haven and Austin made no attempt to acquire Entry **84i**.

Works Consulted

Giroud, Vincent. *Nicolas Nabokov: A Life in Freedom and Music*. Oxford and New York: Oxford University Press, 2015. pp. 187, 193, 202, [447:] *Abbreviations*.

Lubrano, J. & J. *Catalogue* 61. Lloyd Harbor, NY: 2004, lot 175 (with translation).

SBu. pp. 138–39 (14–26 December 1946 and 12–16 January 1947).

86i

(1950). Autograph postcard with photograph, 11 × 8.6 cm, with "Igor Strawinsky / Septembre 1948" printed below on white paper, 14.9 × 10.6 cm. Its reverse side, with five inscribed horizontal lines for the addressee, has printed at lower left: "Aux Editions F. Rouge & Cie S.A., Lausanne / LE MESSAGE D'IGOR STRAWINSKY / par Théodore Strawinsky. / [exemplaire] 338." This side bears an autograph note, 15 August 1950, to Murray Adaskin. (A reduced photocopy, 7.6 × 10.6 cm, of the address side is now mounted below the photograph):

Hollywood Aug 15/50

Dear Mr. Adaskin,
　　How awfully nice of you to send me the charmantes photos of my grand-son Jean (Zizi). It makes here a real pleasure. Thank you so much. All best

Sincerely,
Igor Stravinsky

Acquisition: By kind donation in late 2002 from Dorothea Adaskin.
Provenance: Murray Adaskin.

Commentary

The photograph is identical to one, 11 × 8.4 cm, tipped in and facing the title page of Théodore Stravinsky's *Le Message d'Igor Strawinsky*, published by F. Rouge at Lausanne, November 1948, in an edition limited to 2135 copies, of which 135 were not for sale. For example, "exemplaire 1397," Professor Slim's own copy of

Le Message with the same photograph tipped in, was purchased at Montreal in the summer of 1954.

In mid-August 1950, Igor Stravinsky had just returned to California from Aspen, CO, where he had conducted concerts on 2 and 8 August. Previous to his appointment in 1952 as head of the Music Department at the University of Saskatchewan in Saskatoon, Murray Adaskin had studied composition with Canadian-born Charles Jones (1910–97) in the summers of 1949–51 at Santa Barbara, and with Darius Milhaud (1892–1974) there and at Aspen in 1949 and 1950, both of whom knew Stravinsky. Adaskin probably photographed Stravinsky's grandson John (1945–), nicknamed Zizi, in June of 1950 in Santa Barbara at the Music Academy of the West, where John's father, Soulima, was then teaching.

Works Consulted

Aide, William, and Gordana Lazarevich. "Adaskin, Murray." *The New Grove Dictionary of Music and Musicians*, 2nd ed., vol. 1. Oxford: Grove, 2001. pp. 102–3.

Hanson, Jens. "Adaskin, Murray." *Encyclopedia of Music in Canada*, 2nd ed. Edited by Helmut Kallmann, Gilles Potvin, and Kenneth Winters. Toronto: University of Toronto Press, 1992. pp. 6–7.

Lazarevich, Gordana. *The Musical World of Frances James and Murray Adaskin*. Toronto: University of Toronto Press, 1988. [p. 6] lower plate, and pp. 142–43.

Lederman, Minna, ed. *Stravinsky in the Theater*. New York: Farrar, Straus and Giroux, 1949; repr. New York: Da Capo, 1975, p. 177, offers a different photograph taken in 1948 of three-year-old John Stravinsky, his father, and his grandfather. One such photograph, bearing Igor Stravinsky's autograph dedication, is in SAc, p. 175.

Strawinsky, Théodore. *Le Message d'Igor Strawinsky*. Lausanne: Rouge, 1948.

111i (1962). Signed, folded program, 4 pp., 17 × 12 cm, printed for two performances in Leningrad: Monday and Tuesday, 8 and 9 October 1962, by the Leningrad Philharmonic Symphony Orchestra. Each concert was shared by Stravinsky and Craft. On p. 2, under his portrait, he inscribed "I Stravinsky" in Cyrillic, in black ink. The program has notes in Russian about the works performed.

Acquisition: H. Colin Slim in Berkeley, CA, on 18 February 2017 from J.B. Muns, Berkeley, CA, *Musical Autographs, List 17–01* (January 2017), no. 35 – Muns incorrectly describing therein this program as having taken place in Moscow. Donated by Professor Slim in June 2017.
Provenance: Unknown (Muns owned **111i** from c. 2007).

Commentary

Over the course of a year, thirty thousand people are said to have queued up in Leningrad for tickets to the identical pair of concerts Stravinsky and Craft led there on 8 and 9 October 1962. Stravinsky inscribed his name with such force on the above program (serving for both concerts) that in making the flourish of his final letter, his pen pierced the page! Several photographs show him leading the Leningrad Philharmonic at his first concert.

The program has two parts. It opens with the 1908 *Fireworks* (rev. 1909) conducted by Stravinsky. Craft then led a suite of four movements, translated as: "Prologue," "Swiss Dances," "By the Mill," and "Finale and Epilogue," excerpted from Stravinsky's 1928 *The Fairy's Kiss* – these four movements found in his 1934 *Divertimento / Suite Symphonique*. A photograph shows Craft leading the *Divertimento* on 8 October.

In the second part of the Leningrad program, the composer conducted a suite dated there as 1910 from *Firebird* (the year that his ballet premiered in Paris). The suite he led in 1962 at Leningrad was not the one that concluded with the "Infernal Dance," a suite first performed in Russia on 23 October 1910 by Alexander Ziloti (1863–1945) in St. Petersburg, and published in 1912. As listed by Taruskin, the five movements that Ziloti led differ from the five that Stravinsky led at Leningrad in 1962. The five movements listed in Entry **111i** may be translated as:

1. Introduction. Kastchey's Enchanted Garden.
2. Appearance and Dance of the Firebird.
3. Chorovod [Round Dance] of the [Enchanted] Princesses.
4. Arrival of Kastchey. Infernal Dance by All of Kastchey's Subjects.
5. Lullaby. General Rejoicing.

Although the Leningrad program correctly notes that Stravinsky made a second suite in 1919 from his *Firebird* ballet, this program neither mentions his third suite made in 1945 nor clarifies which of the three suites (1910, 1919, or 1945) he led there in 1962.

According to Libman, "there were no rental charges at Moscow [in late

September and early October] for orchestral parts" (where Stravinsky conducted a *Firebird Suite* and recorded excerpts from his revised 1947 *Petrushka* with the Moscow Philharmonic Orchestra) "because the Russians had their own quite satisfactory materials." However, Craft observed that the orchestra parts for *Capriccio* (which he conducted in Moscow) were "copied from a pirated score, full of mistakes – missing accidentals, wrong clefs."

Whether or not this was also the case for *Firebird* in Leningrad remains unknown. It contradicts jottings about parts that Mario Bois made on 17 September 1962 after the Stravinskys and Craft had arrived in Paris from Israel via Venice, two weeks before the latter three flew to Moscow. Bois, at that time an agent for Boosey & Hawkes in Paris, questioned Stravinsky about the required orchestral materials: "the number of scores, and of string parts" that the composer wanted to take to Moscow. Libman further noted that during the 1960s, Stravinsky often programmed his revised 1945 *Firebird Suite*, even though the errors in it "used to provoke the lengthiest diatribe [from him]." The selections he made from the ballet for his 1945 *Firebird Suite* correspond in only a general way to the five items translated above in Entry **111i**. For example, there is no mention in the latter of Prince Ivan, whose folk melody appears in the 1945 *Suite*, preceding the "Chorovod."

Stravinsky's niece, Xenia Yuryevna (daughter of his deceased older brother, Yury), recalled hearing Stravinsky's rehearsals at Moscow in late September and at Leningrad early in October for *Fireworks* and *The Firebird Suite*, these latter rehearsals in company with Igor Blazhkov (assistant conductor of the Leningrad Philharmonic). Shortly after Stravinsky's final departure on 11 October from Moscow, the composer's great admirer Professor Maria Yudina (1899–1970), a brilliant Moscow pianist and pedagogue, wrote that he "amazed everyone with his conducting, especially *Firebird* in Leningrad; this was the peak of his might."

Works Consulted

Bois, Mario. *Près de Strawinsky 1959–70*. Paris: Marval, 1996. [p. 130].

Craft, Robert. *Stravinsky: Chronicle of a Friendship*, 2nd ed. Nashville, TN, and London: Vanderbilt University Press, 1994. pl. 7 (8 October 1962), pls. btn pp. 302–3, pp. 314–20, 323, 330–39.

Cross, Jonathan. *Igor Stravinsky*. London: Reaktion, 2015. pp. 178–80.

Leiren, Hal [in conversation with Lillian Libman]. "Stravinsky Finds a Typo." *Vancouver Sun* (12 July 1965): 3.

Levitz, Tamara. "Stravinsky's Cold War: Letters About the Composer's Return to Russia, 1960–1963." *Stravinsky and His World*. Edited by Tamara Levitz. Princeton, NJ, and Oxford: Princeton University Press, 2013. pp. 300–2 (letter 28).

Libman, Lillian. *And Music at the Close: Stravinsky's Last Years, a Personal Memoir.* New York: W.W. Norton, 1972. pp. 134,154 (second footnote).

Muns, J.B. *Musical Autographs List 17–01.* Berkeley, CA: January 2017, lot 35.

SBu. pp. 209 (pl. 163), 211 (October 1962).

SD&D. pp. 257–61.

SP&D. pp. 469–70.

SSC. vol. 3. pls. 24–25 btn pp. 242–43.

SSE. pp. 428–29, 460–71.

Stravinskaya, Xenia Yuryevna. *O I.F. Stravinskom i yego blizkikh.* [*About I.F. Stravinsky and His Intimates*]. Leningrad: Muzika, 1978. pp. 133–64, and pl. btn pp. 155–58.

Stravinsky in Moscow 1962. Moscow: Melodiya, the Russian Label. CD 1962.

Stuart, Philip. *Igor Stravinsky – The Composer in the Recording Studio: A Comprehensive Discography.* Westport, CT: Greenwood Press, 1991. p. 72: L20 ("Moscow").

Taruskin, Richard. *Stravinsky and the Russian Traditions.* Berkeley and Los Angeles: University of California Press, 1996. pp. 641–42, and n. 124.

Walsh, Stephen. *Stravinsky, A Creative Spring: Russia and France, 1882–1934.* New York: Alfred A. Knopf, 1999. pp. 150, 544.

White, Eric Walter. *Stravinsky: The Composer and His Works*, 2nd ed. Berkeley and Los Angeles: University of California Press, 1979; repr. 1984. pp. 180–81, 189–90, 354–55.

See also Entries **1i**, 48, 111, and 115.

114i

(1965). Autographed photograph, 26.1 × 23.9 cm, inscribed "I Stravinsky/1965" taken by Barry Glass, 13 July 1965, in Vancouver, BC.

Acquisition: By kind donation on 13 August 2002 from J.E. Horvath, Vancouver. *Provenance*: Mr. Horvath wrote in green ink on the reverse side of his business card accompanying his donation of this photograph: "Taken at Stravinsky's last public performance [13 July 1965 in Vancouver, BC], and signed at the dinner table [in] Mrs. Otto Koerner's house in Vancouver in 1965. He conducted in a winter coat on a specially secured podium. Aug. 13, 2002. [signed:] J.E. Horvath."

This photograph is accompanied by another gift from Mr. Horvath. It is a pen and ink drawing, 13 × 6 cm, described by him: "Drawing of [by] Mrs. Sanelta Molnar Krisztinkevich, late sister of Mrs. Otto Koerner, of Stravinsky conducting in orchestra coat as seen by the audience in 1965. Original in our possession. 13 August 2002."

Commentary

Stamped on the back of its mount is: "Photograph by / Barry Glass, / 353 Vinmore Road / Richmond B.C. Canada." Stravinsky's clothing and activity reveal that Entry **114i**'s photograph was not taken at a performance, but at a rehearsal of the Vancouver Symphony Orchestra for its concerts, 12 and 13 July, during the 1965 Vancouver International Festival. Acquisition of this photograph thus meets a *desideratum* expressed in the 2002 *Annotated Catalogue* (p. 4) for UBC's future collection to include items concerning Stravinsky's second (1965) visit to Vancouver.

Mr. Horvath's remarks on his business card and his description of Mrs. Krisztinkevich's drawing indicate that both Koerner sisters were at Stravinsky's second concert, followed by dinner (late) that evening at the spacious home of the widowed Mrs. Otto (Iby) Koerner (1899–1983) located at 1838 Matthews Avenue in Vancouver's upscale Shaughnessy neighbourhood.

Works Consulted

Cunningham, Rosemary. "A Debt Acknowledged: Iby Koerner's Contribution to Vancouver," *British Columbia History* 39, no. 2 (2006): 12–20.

Helmer, Paul. *Growing with Canada: The Emigré Tradition in Canadian Music.* Montreal and Kingston, London, Ithaca: McGill-Queen's University Press, 2009. pp. 10, 268–69.

RBSC-ARC-1782-1-08 and –07

(1965)

a) Program for the eighth Vancouver International Festival, 12–13 July 1965. Stravinsky and Craft conducted, and each initialled its program.

Acquisition: c. 2013 in Vancouver.
Provenance: Unknown.

Commentary

This program, autographed by Stravinsky and Craft for the Vancouver Festival attendee, reveals the original plan for both performances. Ultimately, the *Symphony in Three Movements* and *Introitus* were deleted. The 1945 *Firebird Suite*, led by its composer, was added to conclude the program.

Works Consulted

"Important Program Changes" (advertisement). *Vancouver Sun* (12 July 1965).

b) Autographed photograph (cropped at right?), 20.5 × 25.5 cm (8 × 10 in.) of Stravinsky conducting a recording rehearsal, probably in New York, 1960s, for Columbia Records, printed on a black background, marked: "2" (lower left), and designated as a Sol Hurok (1888–1974) publicity photograph. Stravinsky signed its lower margin in English in black ink, July 1965, to Hugh Pickett (1913–2006):

> To you, dear Mr. Pickett
> Most sincerely
> I Stravinsky
> July, 1965.

Acquisition: Kevin Madill, UBC Music Librarian, 14 September 2015.
Provenance: Estate of Hugh Pickett, from Love's Auctioneers and Appraisers, Richmond, BC (2015).

Commentary

Confessedly against his better judgment, Hugh Pickett, manager of "Famous Players" in Vancouver, was persuaded by impresario Sol Hurok of "Famous Artists" in New York to engage Stravinsky (and Robert Craft) to conduct the (augmented) Vancouver Symphony Orchestra at the city's eighth International Festival, 12 and 13 July 1965. Years later (in 2002), Pickett stated that "the notoriously hard-to-handle Igor Stravinsky was terrible at first. Really obnoxious. Slowly he came around. He was here four days before we really got to know him."

Pickett's autographed photograph may have resulted from some assistance he was able to offer Stravinsky during an embarrassing episode in 1965 at a dress rehearsal, as recounted by Lillian Libman. An identical photograph – slightly cropped at the right and copyrighted "Sony Classical France" – appeared in a book by Mario Bois published in 1996 that includes many photographs of Stravinsky.

Along with this photograph, which Pickett allowed to be reproduced in a 2002 newspaper interview, he stated that Stravinsky "had a 'friend' [male] who also traveled with him. I got it all very quickly." Pickett could not have meant Craft, whose vaunted heterosexuality abounds in his diaries and journals. Apparently, he meant Lawrence Morton (1904–87), for whom, however, not a smidgeon of evidence exists for any such relationship with Stravinsky. In so alleging, Pickett anticipated Craft's accusation in 2013 of Stravinsky engaging in homosexual relationships, now discredited.

Works Consulted

Bois, Mario. *Près de Strawinsky 1959–70*. Paris: Marval, 1996. p. 141, lower image.

Corn, Alfred. "The Ambidexterity of a Musician." *The Gay & Lesbian Review* 21, no. 1 (January–February 2014): 40–41.

Craft, Robert. *Stravinsky: Discoveries and Memories*. Great Britain: Naxos Books, 2013. pp. 165–73, 175.

–. "Vision in Music: Igor Stravinsky's Own Instructions for Dancing *The Rite of Spring*." *The Times Literary Supplement* (21 June 2013): 13–15, at 14.

Leiren, Hal [in conversation with Lillian Libman]. "Stravinsky Finds a Typo." *Vancouver Sun* (12 July 1965): 3.

Libman, Lillian. *And Music at the Close: Stravinsky's Last Years, a Personal Memoir*. New York: W. W. Norton, 1972. pp. 134, 188.

Mackie, John. "Mr. Impresario," *Vancouver Sun* (17 August 2002): "MIX," H4–H5.

Slim, H. Colin. "Stravinsky in Vancouver, 1917–2017: Concerts, Premieres, Collections." *The Musical Quarterly* (2018): 11–13.

Taruskin, Richard. *Russian Music at Home and Abroad: New Essays*. Oakland: University of California Press, 2016. 9–13.

117i

(1967). Photograph (uninscribed), 23.5 × 19 cm, of Stravinsky and John L. Roberts (1930–) arriving at a reception after a CBC concert, 17 May 1967, at

Massey Hall, Toronto. The photograph was taken by Paul Smith, Toronto.
Acquisition: By kind donation in fall–winter 2002 from Dorothea Adaskin.
Provenance: Murray Adaskin, from John Roberts, Toronto, by letter of 20 June 1967.

Commentary

The photograph is stamped on its reverse side: "paul smith / Photography / 546 Richmond Street West / Toronto 28, Canada 369-6003 / Reorder No. 67-206-49" and was later reproduced by Roberts on p. 32 of his essay cited below. The photograph records the last time that Stravinsky conducted anywhere. UBC's photograph is accompanied by Roberts's letter to Murray Adaskin and a Toronto newspaper clipping from 1982.

Works Consulted

Littler, William. "Stravinsky Anniversary Is One Long Party." *Toronto Star* (29 May 1982): F12.

Litwack, Linda. "Roberts, John." *Encyclopedia of Music in Canada*, 2nd ed. Edited by Helmut Kallmann, Gilles Potvin, and Kenneth Winters. Toronto, Buffalo, and London: University of Toronto Press, 1992. p. 1136.

Roberts, John [L.]. "Stravinsky and the CBC." *Les cahiers canadiens de musique / The Canada Music Book* 4–5 (Spring–Summer 1972): 32–36.

122i

(1981). Program booklet of the Royal Ballet, performing at the Royal Opera House, Covent Garden, Monday, London, 2 February 1981, 22.9 × 13 cm. The performance included *Les Noces*, with a restoration of its original 1923 choreography by Bronislava Nijinska. Among the solo singers was UBC graduate Milla Andrew (1930–).

Acquisition: Donated by Professor Slim in June 2017.
Provenance: H. Colin Slim, London, February 1981.

Commentary

Living in London during a 1981 sabbatical from the University of California, Irvine, Professor Slim was attracted by an opportunity to see a revival of Nijinska's choreography for *Les Noces*. Attending a performance on 2 February 1981 at the

Royal Opera House, he was delighted to see and to hear Milla Andrew sing in *Les Noces* (as she had at its Canadian premiere led by him in April 1952 at UBC's Brock Hall). On 10 April 1953, as conductor of the Vancouver Junior Symphony, he had also led her in "Air de Salomé" from Massenet's *Hérodiade*. Moving to England in the early 1960s, she went on to a distinguished worldwide stage and recording career in opera.

Works Consulted

Adaskin, Harry. *A Fiddler's Choice: Memoirs 1938 to 1980.* Vancouver, BC: November House, 1982. pl. 16 btn pp. 94–95.

Anonymous. "Andrew, Milla." *Encyclopedia of Music in Canada*, 2nd ed. Edited by Helmut Kallmann, Gilles Potvin, and Kenneth Winters. Toronto, Buffalo, and London: University of Toronto Press, 1992. p. 24.

Slim, H. Colin. *Annotated Catalogue.* Entry 90, p. 270.

123i

(1982). First day cover, 9.3 × 16.4 cm, postmarked "New York, zip 10001, Nov 18 1982," bearing a two-cent USA postage stamp of Stravinsky and, at the left side of the envelope, an anonymous caricature by "Krainik '82" of the composer, and printed at the right side: "AURORA COVERS 5." On the rear side of the envelope is stamped "157 of 228."

Acquisition: By kind donation from UBC Professor Jesse Read, who purchased it in December 2001 from Kok, a dealer in Amsterdam.
Provenance: Unknown.

Commentary

The 1982 Krainik caricature is based upon a 1957 photograph taken of Stravinsky in New York listening to a playback of one of his recordings. The photograph was reproduced in 1963 and appears on the dustcover of the Stravinsky-Craft book containing it.

Works Consulted

SD&D. pl. 13 btn pp. 160–61, and dustcover.

Slim, H. Colin. *Annotated Catalogue.* Entry 123.

SECTION 2

Corrections and Additions
to Slim, Annotated Catalogue (2002)

CORRECTIONS AND ADDITIONS

p. 3, **add**: On Alexis Fyodorovich Kall, see H. Colin Slim, "Unknown Words and Music, 1939–44 by Stravinsky for His Longtime Friend, Dr. Alexis Kall," *Words on Music: Essays in Honor of Andrew Porter on the Occasion of His 75th Birthday*, ed. David Rosen and Claire Brook (Hillsdale, NY: Pendragon Press, 2003), pp. 300–19.

p. 4, following: "in Paris that June." **add**: Stravinsky's two Chopin orchestrations were first heard in Canada by Vancouver balletomanes at the old CPR Opera House on 15 January 1917; see the *Vancouver Sun* (10 January 1917): 5.

p. 5, **add**: Concerning Stravinsky's 1946–47 revision of *Petrushka*, see Entry **83i**.

p. 6, **add**: SP&RK, vol. 3, p. 851, mistakenly locates the 1952 Canadian premiere of *Les Noces* led by Professor Slim as in Montreal, rather than in Vancouver (at UBC, Brock Hall).

p. 10, n. 13 (on p. 17), **add**: Craft's avowal, *Memoirs*, p. 60, that he "was the sole born-and-bred American" friend of Stravinsky requires correction in view of friendships in the early 1940s with the McQuoid, Sample, and Andersson families; about the latter two, see H. Colin Slim, "Lessons with Stravinsky: The Notebook of Earnest Andersson (1878–1943)," JAMS 62, no. 2 (Summer 2009): 323–412.

p. 11, no. 7, **see also** Entry **83i**, i.e., "Stravinsky's own signed and annotated printed copy of *Petrushka*."

p. 12, paragraph beginning "An examination…," following "will be *unica*," **add**: "above all, Entry **41ii** with its extraordinary handwritten marginalia."

pp. 12–13, **add**: Dagmar Godowsky (ex Entry **47i**).

p. 14, "barbarous practice," revise and **add**: Entries 100 and **66i** testify all too eloquently to this barbarous practice.

pp. 26, 34 (Entries 1, 4), to each **add**: see SP&RK, vol. 3, p. 894 (index: Calvocoressi).

pp. 43, 46, 50 (Entries 7, 8, 9), to each **add**: see SP&RK, vol. 3, p. 894 (index: Casella).

pp. 46, 54 (Entries 8, 10), to each **add**: see SP&RK, vol. 3, p. 915 (index: Freund).

pp. 46, 75, 148 (Entries 8, 17, 37), to each **add**: see SP&RK, vol. 3, p. 892 (index: Diaghilev).

p. 46 (Entry 8), to Works Consulted **add**: Casella, Alfredo. "Igor Strawinsky e la sua arte." *La riforma musicale* III, nos. 10–11 (7–14 March 1915): 1–2.

p. 52 (Entry 10), line 7 from bottom, **correct**: "*Japaense*" to "*Japanese.*"

p. 59 (Entry 11), **add**: see SP&RK, vol. 3, p. 909 (index: Rouché).

p. 63 (Entry 12), **add**: see SP&RK, vol. 3, p. 910 (index: Sacharoff) and especially no. 1978 (i.e., the same as Entry 12).

pp. 71, 75, 204 (Entries 15, 17, 64), to each **add**: see SP&RK, vol. 3, p. 908 (index: Roland-Manuel).

p. 73 (Entry 16), **add**: see SP&RK, vol. 3, p. 898 (index: Lion).

p. 75 (Entry 17), **add**: further on the character of Diaghilev, see Charles M. Joseph, *Stravinsky & Balanchine* (New Haven and London: Yale University Press, 2002), p. 34.

p. 76 (Entry 18), at line 12 of Russian transliteration **insert**: "menee" between "mne" and "stydno"; at line 13 **correct**: "drugaya" to "drugoe"; at line 3 of translation, following "right away" **add**: "upon your arrival." These alterations are courtesy of Professor Richard Taruskin.

p. 99 (Entry 21), to Works Consulted **add**: Mazo, Margarita. "Stravinsky's 'Les Noces' and Russian Village Wedding Ritual." JAMS 43, no. 1 (Spring 1990): 90–142.

pp. 109, 120, 123 (Entries 23, 26, 27), to each **add**: see SP&RK, vol. 3, p. [920] (index: Janacopulos). **Add**: further, see Craft's (undocumented and possibly erroneous) speculation about an affair between the two, postulated in "An Interview with Robert Craft. Conversation with Robert Craft," *Areté* 24 (Winter 2007): 34–35, and in Robert Craft, *Stravinsky: Discoveries and Memories* (Great Britain: Naxos Books, 2013), pp. 176–77.

p. 106 (Entry 23), line 4 from bottom: Staal's name was Alexis; thus, to "A" **add**: "lexis."

p. 107 (Entry 23), line 19, **add**: Robert Craft, reviewing Walsh's *Stravinsky, A Creative Spring*, vol. 1, in *MQ* 85 (2001): 397, and in Craft, *Stravinsky: Discoveries and Memories* (Great Britain: Naxos Books, 2013), p. 176, states that Stravinsky and Janacopulos first met in Switzerland during World War I, late 1914 or 1915.

p. 113 (Entry 24), **add**: see SP&RK, vol. 3, p. 895 (index: Kibalchich), especially nos. 1082 (= Entry 24), 1123, 1147, 1497.

p. 116 (Entry 25), **add**: see SP&RK, vol. 3, p. 896 (index: Cocteau).

p. 135 (Entry 32), **add**: further on the Murphys and Picasso, see ILM, p. 219.

p. 136 (Entry 33), **add**: see SP&RK, vol. 3, p. 913 (index: Stravinsky, F.I.).

pp. 139–40 (Entry 34), **add**: see SP&RK, vol. 3, pp. 906 (index: Polignac), 909 (index: Satie). A reproduction in Michael Oliver, *Igor Stravinsky* (London: Phaidon, 1995), p. 51, correctly dates the dual image as 1910, as does the one made by Wikimedia Commons and printed in "Playbill," Program Notes for Cal Performances, University of California, Berkeley, Saturday, 8 October 2016, p. 34.

p. 143 (Entry 35), **add**: see SP&RK, vol. 3, p. 896 (index: Kochanski), especially their mutual correspondence in nos. 1238, 1257, 1325, and 1327 (=Entry 35).

p. 146 (Entry 36), **add**: see SP&RK, vol. 3, p. 907 (index: Rabeneck), especially nos. 1348a (=Entry 36) and 1603.

p. 148, **add**: Entry 37 (in Russian) is lacking in SP&RK, vol. 3. See SP&RK, vol. 3, p. 912 (index: Stravinsky, Vera).

p. 151 (Entry 38), **add**: see SP&RK, vol. 3, p. 885 (index: Bottenheim).

p. 153 (Entry 39), **add**: the Fruhauf drawing was twice reproduced in a Danish newspaper, *Dagens nyheder*: 1 May and 26 September 1935; see H. Colin Slim, "From Copenhagen and Paris: A Stravinsky Photograph-Autograph at the University of British Columbia," *Notes: Quarterly Journal of the Music Library Association* 59, no. 3 (March 2003): 548–49. It was also reproduced in Lloyd Dykk, "Stravinsky Collection Goes to UBC / Legacy of a Musical Giant," *Vancouver Sun* (30 March 2002): A1.

pp. 159, 208, 215 (Entries 40, 65, 69), to each **add**: see SP&RK, vol. 3, p. 894 (index: Kahl), a photograph of him in 1898 (btn pp. 432–33), and especially their mutual correspondence from 15 January 1935 in nos. 1782, 1785–86, 1789, 1791, 1801, 1808, 1831, 1839–40, 1851, 1854, 1868, 1873, 1875, 1891, 1893–94, 1910, 1912–13, 1924, 1938, 1945, 1963–64, 1969; see also, SP&RK, vol. 3, p. 908 (index: Robinson, Edward).

p. 161 (Entry 41), **add:** see SP&RK, vol. 3, p. 892 (index: Dushkin).

pp. 163, 165 (Entries 42, 43), to each **add**: see SSE, pp. 21–26.

p. 176 (Entry 45), **add**: Perhaps dancer Aída Mastrazzi and conductor-composer Juan José Castro both attended the duo-piano recital on 2 May 1936 given by Stravinsky and his son at the Teatro Colón; see Entry **43i**.

p. 177 (Entry 45), **add**: see SP&RK, vol. 3, p. 895 (index: Castro). The Slim item cited on p. 177 was published in 2004, pp. 447–58. For photographs of Stravinsky, Soulima, and Ocampo, see Tamara Levitz, "Igor the Angeleno: The Mexican Connection – Dancing on the Volcano: Argentina 1936," in Tamara Levitz, ed., *Stravinsky and His World* (Princeton, NJ: Princeton University Press, 2013), pp. 153–60.

p. 183 (Preliminary Remarks to Entries 48–60), **add**: Stravinsky used the same paper, BFK Rives (p. 183), for copying some music in 1936; see Slim, "From Copenhagen and Paris: A Stravinsky Photograph-Autograph at the University of British Columbia," *Notes: Quarterly Journal of the Music Library Association* 59, no. 3 (March 2003): 548.

p. 187 (Entry 49), **add**: see also Entry **83i**.

p. 196 (Entry 61), **add**: see SP&RK, vol. 3, p. 912 (index: Stravinsky, Sviatoslav Soulima); for another example of Soulima's signature, see Entry **43i**.

p. 199 (Entry 63), **add**: Stravinsky used the same photograph in November 1944, inscribing it to Walter de Bourg; see *Autographen Katalog* 916 (Basel: Erasmushaus, May 2003), p. 87 (lot 191, 4000 Swiss francs); see also SP&RK, vol. 3, p. 890 (index: Gui). Victoria Ocampo was the *diseuse* in the Florence performance; see Tamara Levitz, *Modernist Mysteries: Perséphone* (Oxford and New York: Oxford University Press, 2012), p. 618 (n. 153).

p. 203 (Entry 64), **add**: see SSE, pp. 91–96. For Stravinsky's acquaintance from 1938 with Jean Marx, see Joan Evans, "Stravinsky's Music in Hitler's Germany," JAMS 56, no. 3 (Fall 2003): 572.

p. 206 (Entry 65), **add**: Stravinsky had paid Païchadze to extract parts from Tchaikovsky's first and second symphonies; see SP&RK, vol. 3, p. 670 (no. 1926), and ILM, p. 79 (n. 51).

p. 208 (Entry 65), **add**: see Entry **66i** and SP&RK, vol. 3, p. 902 (index: Monteux), and especially their mutual communication (through Kall), signalled in nos. 1839, 1891, 1893, 1938, and 1969.

p. 214 (Entry 68), **add**: For the 1946–47 revision of *Petrushka*, see Entry **83i**.

p. 215 (Entry 69), **add**: further about Kall, see H. Colin Slim, "Unknown Words and Music, 1939–44 by Stravinsky for His Longtime Friend, Dr. Alexis Kall," *Words on Music: Essays in Honor of Andrew Porter on the Occasion of His 75th Birthday*, ed. David Rosen and Claire Brook (Hillsdale, NY: Pendragon Press, 2003), pp. 300–19.

pp. 222–24 (Entry 72), **add**: An original print of Hoyningen-Huene's photo, inscribed "A Monsieur / Jantos / Baruro / Sincères / Conaissance de / I Strawinsky / Rio / le ii.VI..36," was offered in Lisa Cox, *Music Catalogue* 43 (Spring 2003), lot 105. For a version in reverse, autographed by Stravinsky in 1942, see Entry **72i**.

p. 225 (Entry 73), in line 10 **insert**: "Elliot" between "Professor" and "Forbes."

pp. 231–32 (Entry 75), **add**: Information by Charles M. Joseph, *Stravinsky Inside Out* (New Haven and London: Yale University Press, 2001), p. 19, concerning Stravinsky's so-called arrest in 1940 in Boston; and by Joseph, *Stravinsky &*

Balanchine (New Haven and London: Yale University Press, 2002), p. 175; and by Robert Craft in SM&C, rev. single-volume ed. (London: Faber and Faber, 2002), p. 216, is incorrect, as are Craft's two dates of 1940 on p. 234; nor was there a repeat performance of *Firebird* "on the 30th." Further on Entries 75 and 76, see H. Colin Slim, "Stravinsky's Four Star-Spangled Banners and His 1941 Christmas Card," *The Musical Quarterly* 89, nos. 2–3 (Summer–Fall 2006): 321–447.

p. 235 (Entry 76), **add**: further on Hammond, a "composition pupil of Nadia Boulanger in Paris in the 1920s when he met Stravinsky," see ILM, p. 118. By Christmas of 1941, Hammond was a neighbour of Stravinsky in Hollywood.

p. 236 (Entry 77) in line 5 **correct**: "thigs" to "things."

p. 251 (Entry 81), **add**: see also Don Rayno, *Paul Whiteman: Pioneer in American Music, Volume II: 1930–1967* (Lanham, MD, Toronto, and Plymouth, UK: Scarecrow Press, 2009).

p. 253 (Entry 82), **add**: see the inscribed photograph: "Pour Monsieur / Walter de Bourg / avec tous mes / voeux d'un bon / et heureux / retour en Suisse / I Strawinsky / Hollywood, / Nov. 1944" offered in *Autographen Katalog* 916 (Basel: Erasmushaus, May 2003), pp. 86–87 (lot 191), thus revealing that de Bourg did not leave the USA before November 1944.

pp. 252–54, before and after Entry 82 **add**: de Bourg Entries **79i** (typed letter, January 1944) and **82i** (empty envelope, November 1944).

p. 256 (Entry 100), **add**: on Hans von Benda, see Joan Evans, "Stravinsky's Music in Hitler's Germany" JAMS 56, no. 3 (Fall 2003): 561.

pp. 260–63 (Entry 86), in Commentary, on p. 261, first paragraph, lines 5–6, **correct** the inscription: "To Merle Armitage / my wonderful ar- / tist manager / in gratitude / I Strawinsky / Los Angeles / 29 II 35." **Add**: Charles M. Joseph, *Stravinsky Inside Out* (New Haven and London: Yale University Press, 2001), p. 25, seems unaware that the (first) English translation to which he refers was by Dr. Kall. See H. Colin Slim, "Unknown Words and Music, 1939–44 by Stravinsky for His Longtime Friend, Dr. Alexis Kall," *Words on Music: Essays in Honor of Andrew Porter on the Occasion of His 75th Birthday*, ed. David Rosen and Claire Brook (Hillsdale, NY: Pendragon Press, 2003), p. 309.

p. 267 (Entry 88), to Commentary **add**: the 8 October 1951 performance with Hessenland's narration in German is available on CD 1184, no. 1 (Kensington, CA: Music & Arts Program of America, Inc., 2006), bands 11–16.

p. 270 (Entry 90), to Commentary, following "lively reading." **add**: A 1952 UBC yearbook, *The Totem* 43, p. 61, "Special Events Program," offers two photographs of H. Colin Slim rehearsing *Les Noces.*

p. 274 (Entry 91), to Works Consulted **add**: anonymous, "Special Events Program," *The* [UBC] *Totem* 43 (1952): 61 (two lower photographs); and **add**: Entry **122i**.

p. 274 (Entry 91), **correct**: "Dykl" to "Dykk."

p. 276 (Entry 92), to Commentary following "rarely acknowledged" **add**: and also wrongly dated, for example, "Calendar," *Los Angeles Times* (15 May 1982): 1.

p. 280 (Entry 95), **correct**: The letter is [**add**:] unpublished [etc.]; see SSE, p. 309.

p. 282 (Entry 95), following "Deeply upset:" **add**: Craft, ILM, p. 160, notes that in January 1954 he suggested that Stravinsky should set Thomas's poem.

pp. 285–94 (Entries 97, 98, 99), **add**: on Weissberger, see also SSE, pp. 550ff.; and ILM, pp. 180, 259, 290, 301, 304, 317 (n. 7), 323, 330.

pp. 294–98 (Entry 100), at p. 297, line 4, following "Warsaw" **change**: "he" to "Stravinsky." At p. 298 to Works Consulted **add**: Prokofiev, Sergey. "19 January, 1925." *1924–1933 Prodigal Son.* Vol. 3 of *Sergey Prokofiev Diaries.* Translated and annotated by Anthony Phillips. Ithaca, NY: Cornell University Press, 2013. pp. 130–31 (citing Stravinsky previously having drawn his *left* hand [*sic*] for a Warsaw hostess, presumably Madame Grossman).

p. 301 (Entry 101), **add**: further on this concert, see SSE, pp. 364–65.

p. 303 (Entry 102), **add**: further on this singer, see Doda Conrad, *Dodascalies: Ma chronique du XXe siècle* (Arles: Actes Sud, 1997).

p. 305 (Entry 103), **add**: partially reproduced (after the copy in the Sacher Foundation, Basel) in Charles M. Joseph, *Stravinsky Inside Out* (New Haven and

London: Yale University Press, 2001), p. 203; and in his *Stravinsky & Balanchine* (New Haven and London: Yale University Press, 2002), p. 404 (n. 2). Further about Kirstein's (successful) efforts, see Martin Duberman, *The Worlds of Lincoln Kirstein* (New York: Knopf, 2007), p. 527, and about the Dartington excursions, see ILM, p. 188.

pp. 305–9 (Entry 104), **add**: on the Eliot correspondence, see ILM, pp. 194, 199; and on Ocampo, pp. 98, 121, 244, 245 (n. 4), 315. Charles M. Joseph, *Stravinsky Inside Out* (New Haven and London: Yale University Press, 2001), p. 124, states, however, that Stravinsky first met Huxley in 1928 in London. Further, see SSE, pp. 358–59, 397–98. Weissberger wrote to Sweden on 3 July 1958; see Stravinsky's letter to him, 14 July 1959, in J.A. Stargardt, *Catalog* 673 (Berlin: 11–12 June 2002), lot 988.

p. 310 (Entry 106), at bottom of page, following "1956" **add**: [*sic*].

pp. 316–17 (Entry 108), **add**: Charles M. Joseph, *Stravinsky Inside Out* (New Haven and London: Yale University Press, 2001), p. 242, mentions Stravinsky's letter of 20 February 1959 requesting from Broude a copy of Krenek's *Tonal Counterpoint*.

pp. 318–21 (Entry 109), **add:** see also ILM, pp. 246–47.

p. 323 (Entry 110), **add**: Charles M. Joseph, *Stravinsky Inside Out* (New Haven and London: Yale University Press, 2001), p. 157, and his *Stravinsky & Balanchine* (New Haven and London: Yale University Press, 2002), p. 408 (n. 17), reproduce the text of the telegram from the version appearing in the *New York Herald Tribune*.

pp. 324–27 (Entry 111), **add**: all twelve Fehl photographs of Stravinsky rehearsing members of the New York Philharmonic at Lewisohn Stadium in New York are reproduced in Lloyd Dykk, "Stravinsky Collection Goes to UBC," *Vancouver Sun* (30 May 2002): A6. To text at p. 326 **add**: Craft, ILM, p. 257, reports that "during rehearsals [at Lewisohn Stadium] Marian Ostrovsky photographed Stravinsky without letup." A photograph by Allyn Baum cited by Craft at p. 325 in Entry 111, showing Stravinsky conducting the concert, also appears in Anthony Tommasini, "That Summer of Stravinsky's 'Spring'," *New York Times* (5 September 2015): C1, C3, at C3.

p. 328 (Entry 112), **add**: on Dr. Edel, see ILM, pp. 79, 109, 127–28, 148, 165, 250, 256, 273, 432.

pp. 329–32 (Entry 113), **add**: Craft, ILM, p. 273, observes that Dr. Edel took the Stravinskys to dinner with Kohner (on 14 July 1964) "to discuss the possible use of Stravinsky's public-domain music in Dino de Laurentiis's *The Bible.*" Craft was apparently unaware that Entry 113 is dated 27 April 1964. On Montapert, see also, Craft, ILM, p. 290, and his *Stravinsky: Discoveries and Memories* (Great Britain: Naxos Books, 2013), pp. 206, 228–32.

pp. 337–38 (Entry 116): **add**: Misspelling "McDowall," Craft, ILM, 133, notes that the photographer was friends with Miranda Masocco Davis, who seems to have introduced McDowall to the Stravinskys. Another possibility for "Bill" might be Bill Bowman: "among their [the Stravinskys'] closest New York friends," ILM, p. 74 (n. 38).

pp. 339–42 (Entry 117), **add**: on Mrs. Stalvey, see also ILM, pp. 290, 303.

pp. 343–44 (Entry 119), **add**: Stravinsky's "fourteen" days of treatments during trips to and stays, 2–28 November, in the hospital, cited in Robert Craft, *Stravinsky: Discoveries and Memories* (Great Britain: Naxos Books, 2013), pp. 226–27, conflict with the number of them cited in Vera's published diary for November, the composer returning home on 28 November.

p. 349 (Entry 122), **add**: see SP&RK, vol. 3, p. 883 (index: Balanchine), and especially Charles M. Joseph, *Stravinsky & Balanchine* (New Haven and London: Yale University Press, 2002), *passim.*

INDEX

Library and Archives Canada Cataloguing in Publication

University of British Columbia. Library. Special Collections and University Archives Division, issuing body
        Supplement to the Annotated catalogue of the H. Colin Slim Stravinsky collection : donated by Professor Slim to the University of British Columbia.

By H. Colin Slim.
Includes bibliographical references and index.
ISBN 978-0-88865-295-9 (softcover)

        1. Stravinsky, Igor, 1882-1971--Archives--Catalogs. 2. University of British Columbia. Library. Special Collections and University Archives Division--Catalogs. I. Slim, H. Colin (Harry Colin), author II. Title. II. Title: Stravinsky collection.

ML134.S96S55 2018   016.78092   C2018-904292-3

The Library gratefully acknowledges the financial support and collecting commitment of Dr. H. Colin Slim, which made the *Annotated Catalogue* (2002) and this supplement to it possible. This supplement is not for sale. It is distributed *gratis* to conservatories of music, scholarly institutions, and individuals with an interest in Igor Stravinsky. Its intent is to increase an appreciation of the composer's achievements and to stimulate further research about him and his works.

PRINTED AND BOUND IN CANADA BY Hemlock Printers
SET IN Bembo and Univers
DESIGNED BY Steedman Design
EDITED AND INDEXED BY Greg Gibson
COVER PHOTO BY Eric Skipsey, 1952

THE UNIVERSITY OF BRITISH COLUMBIA LIBRARY
1961 East Mall
Vancouver, BC, V6T 1Z1
604 822 6375
www.library.ubc.ca